The Fizz-Buzz

Written by Roderick Hunt
Illustrated by Alex Brychta

OXFORD
UNIVERSITY PRESS

Read these words

zip   fizz

buzz   off

zap   puff

Dad had a Zip-zap.

Let it off, Dad.

Off it went.

Dad had a Fizz-buzz.

But it did not go off.

The Fizz-buzz went puff.

puff

The Fizz-buzz went off!

Up it went.

Dad fell in the mud.

Talk about the story

Spot the difference

Find the five differences in the two pictures.

Less Mess

Written by Roderick Hunt
Illustrated by Alex Brychta

OXFORD
UNIVERSITY PRESS

Read these words

fuss	less
mess	jam
jug	mix

"Put it all in," said Dad.

"Fill up the jug."

"Put in lots of jam," said Dad.

"Mix it all up," said Dad.

Dad did not put the lid on.

"Mop it up," said Mum. "No fuss."

"We got rid of the mess,"
said Dad.

Talk about the story

Maze

Help the firework get up into the sky.